Curriculum Visi...

Spelling
Book 3

Sarah Lindsay

Curriculum Visions
Spelling

Teacher's Resource Book
There is a Teacher's Resource Book to accompany this Pupil Book.

Dedicated Web Site
There's more information about other great Curriculum Visions resources and a wealth of supporting material available at:
www.CurriculumVisions.com

Author
Sarah Lindsay

Art Director
Duncan McCrae

Senior Designer
Adele Humphries

Editors
Robert Anderson and Gillian Gatehouse

Illustrations
Mark Stacey

Designed and produced by
EARTHSCAPE EDITIONS

Printed in China by
WKT Company Ltd

This product is manufactured from sustainable managed forests. For every tree cut down at least one more is planted.

**First published in 2006 by
Atlantic Europe Publishing Company Ltd
Reprinted June 2006**

Text copyright © Sarah Lindsay 2006

The right of Sarah Lindsay to be identified as the author of this work has been asserted by her in accordance with the Copyright, Designs and Patents Act 1988.

Illustrations and design copyright © 2006 Atlantic Europe Publishing Company Ltd

**Curriculum Visions Spelling Book 3
A CIP record for this book is available from the British Library.**

ISBN-10: 1-86214-512-1
ISBN-13: 978-1-86214-512-2

Contents

Unit 1

a–e ai ay

ray

lake

train

lake	raid	ray	train
flake	afraid	spray	sprain
lame	rain	way	shame
flame	drain	sway	display

Finding words

A Write the words to match the pictures.

tr__n   r__n   fl_k_   r__

B Write these words in your book, filling in the missing letters.

sh_p_   br__n   dism__   tr__

w__   displ__   wh_l_

The word list will help you with some of the words!

4

Using words

A Copy these words.

afraid	match	tray	explain	
packet	frame	lamb	pray	pavement

Tick the words where the letter **a** in the word makes the same sound as the **ay** in d**ay**.

B Write the words you have ticked in some sentences.

Shh...
You should have ticked six words.

Puzzle corner

When **ing** is added to a verb that ends in **e**, the **e** is dropped.

bake + ing = bak**ing**

A **verb** is usually an action word.

Add **ing** to each word to make the word into a verb.

What are we doing? The words in the box will help you.

shake	race	parade
wake	decorate	wave

5

Unit 2

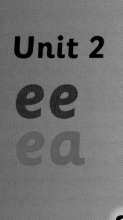

ee
ea

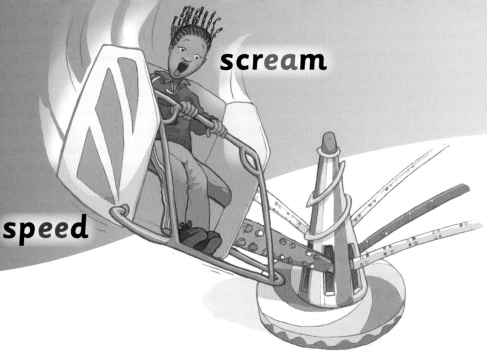

scream

speed

seed	beak	sheet	cream
weed	leak	sleet	dream
bleed	weak	street	scream
speed	speak	sweet	stream

Finding words

A Write the words to match the pictures.

str__t   b__k   sw__t   str__m

B Write these words in your book, filling in the missing letters.

fl__t   st__m   n__t   b__

sp__k   dr__m   sl__t

The word list will help you with some of the words!

6

Using words

peach	leap	head	spread	weave
cheat	steam	seat	read	thread
instead	leave	beast	dead	flea

A Sort these words. Make two lists.

In the first list write the words that sound like **ea** in t**ea**m.

Put the other words in another list – they all sound like the **ea** in h**ea**d.

B Write some sentences using four of the words in the first list.

team

head

One word in the box can be written in both lists... which word is it?

Puzzle corner

Look at the picture.
Add the missing syllable to finish each word.

Remember that each **beat** of a word is called a syllable!

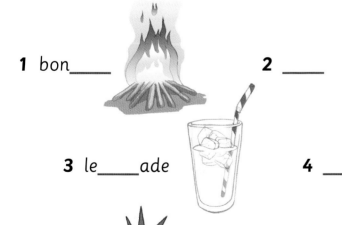

1 bon____

2 ____

3 le____ade

4 ____pet

5 sig____

6 to____to

Unit 3

ie
i-e
y
igh

cry

bright

bride

pie

die	hide	cry	high
lie	bride	shy	light
pie	time	spy	bright
tie	slime	style	flight

Finding words

A Write the words to match the pictures.

sp_   fl___t   p__   h_d_

B Write these words in your book, filling in the missing letters.

br___t   k_t_   dr_   l__

wh_   r___t   dr_v_

The word list will help you with some of the words!

Using words

In this picture there are eight pictures of words
that sound like **i** in l**ie**, p**i**p**e**, t**igh**t and tr**y**.

A Write the words you find.

> This might help…
> there are two
> words from each
> spelling pattern.

B Write a short story about the picture.
Try to include all the **i** words you have found.

Puzzle corner

Copy the words. Mark them with a tick or a cross.

> Please will
> you mark my
> spelling test?

peeple ☐	**should** ☐
where ☐	**skool** ☐
nigt ☐	**laugh** ☐
anuther ☐	**becose** ☐

> How many did
> I get right?

Next to the words that are wrong, write the correct spelling.
Use a dictionary to help if you need to.

Unit 4

**o–e
oa
ow**

road

yellow

rose

nose	load	blow	throat
rose	road	snow	smoke
bone	soak	throw	stroke
phone	croak	yellow	tomorrow

Finding words

A Write the words to match the pictures.

ph_n_   yell_ _   n_s_   r_ _d

B Write these words in your book, filling in the missing letters.

fl_ _t   arr_ _   t_ _d   b_ _

s_ _k   tomorr_ _   sm_k_

The word list will help you with some of the words!

Using words

frown   tomorrow   bow   know   window   town   grow   growl
crowd   row   flower   shadow   arrow   crown   flow   clown

A Sort these words. Make two lists. In the first list write the words that sound like **ow** in c**ow**.

cow

Put the other words in another list – they all sound like the **ow** in sn**ow**.

Now can you add two more words to each list?

There are two words that can be written in both lists. Which are they?

sn**ow**

B Write some sentences using four of the words from the second list.

Puzzle corner

Copy the table.
Sort the words into the table using their first letter.

goat sparrow hole mow stone throw

b	g	h	m	s	t
bow					

bow toast grow boat mole hose

Add another o–e, oa or ow word to each column.
Use your reading book to help.

Unit 5

oo ew u–e ue

chew
costume
food
blue

food	dew	tube	blue
pool	chew	flute	glue
spoon	screw	prune	rescue
tooth	shrew	costume	statue

Finding words

A Write the words to match the pictures.

 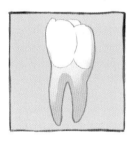  

scr_ _   t_ _th   t_b_   gl_ _

B Write these words in your book, filling in the missing letters.

resc_ _   cl_ _   cr_ _   pr_n_

g_ _se   cost_m_   h_ _p

The word list will help you with some of the words!

Using words

wood	loop	moose	good	wool
rook	room	hoot	foot	cook
soot	spoon	pool	hood	moon

zoom

A Sort these words. Make two lists.

In the first list write the words that sound like **oo** in z**oo**m.

Put the other words in another list – they all need to sound like **oo** in b**oo**k.

B Write some sentences using four of the words in the first list.

book

Puzzle corner

Copy the definitions.
Match each word with the correct definition.
The picture will give you a clue.

dowry **nautical**

conservation  **stifle**

1 protecting things that need protecting
2 anything to do with ships and sailing
3 to try to stop something
4 a gift of money or goods

13

Unit 6
le

jungle

stumble

angle	bustle	bundle	bramble
tangle	rustle	candle	scramble
jungle	hustle	handle	grumble
single	thistle	dwindle	stumble

Finding words

A Write a **le** word to match each picture.

Shh… You will find the words in the word list!

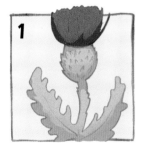

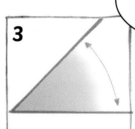

B Write a **le** word to rhyme with each of these words.

1 mumble   **2** twinkle   **3** bristle   **4** scribble

Using words

A Answer these clues with a **le** word.
The pictures will help you.

1 a type of sale

2 the top of an apple pudding

3 can be found floating on bath water

4 often needed to move a boat through water

5 a shape

6 cooked eggs when they
are mixed together well

B Choose three **le** words.
Write a clue for each of them.

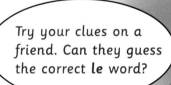

> Try your clues on a friend. Can they guess the correct **le** word?

Puzzle corner

Find a **synonym** for each of these words in the wordsearch.

1 like   **2** big
3 nice   **4** good
5 push

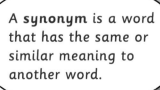

> A **synonym** is a word that has the same or similar meaning to another word.

p	s	t	y	l	v	d
g	h	g	j	r	q	s
l	o	g	s	a	m	k
a	v	t	b	n	j	i
r	e	n	j	o	y	n
g	r	e	a	t	i	d
e	a	d	t	w	h	m

Unit 7

disconnect

untidy

un
dis

unable	**dis**agree	**un**easy	**dis**appear
uncover	**dis**like	**un**happy	**dis**comfort
unborn	**dis**obey	**un**kind	**dis**connect
undress	**dis**trust	**un**tidy	**dis**honest

Finding words

A Add **un** or **dis** to each of the words to match the picture.

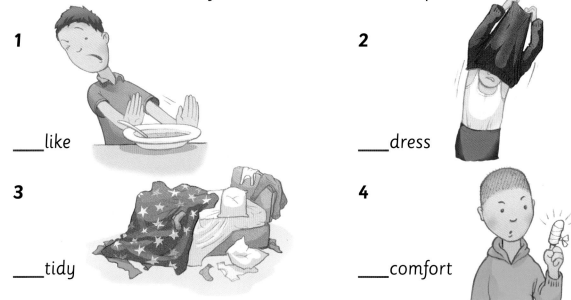

1

____like

2

____dress

3

____tidy

4

____comfort

B Write each of the words you have made in a sentence.

Using words

The letters **un** and **dis** are prefixes.
A **prefix** is added to a word to change its meaning.

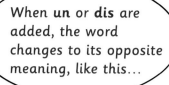

When **un** or **dis** are added, the word changes to its opposite meaning, like this…

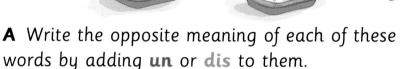

cover   **un**cover

A Write the opposite meaning of each of these words by adding **un** or **dis** to them.

1 fold	**2** please	**3** clean
4 heard	**5** continue	**6** well

B Check the new words you have written in a dictionary.
Tick the words you have spelt correctly.

Puzzle corner

A **thesaurus** is similar to a dictionary.
The words are arranged alphabetically.
It gives us **synonyms** of words.

Do you remember what a **synonym** is?
It's a word with the same or similar meaning to another word.

Use a thesaurus to help you find three synonyms for each word.

Keyword	Synonyms		
fall			
run			
strong			
wet			
put			

Unit 8

air
are
ear
ere

hairy

stare

there

pear

ch**air**	c**are**	b**ear**	th**ere**
h**air**	gl**are**	p**ear**	wh**ere**
f**air**	sh**are**	w**ear**	downst**air**s
d**air**y	st**are**	sw**ear**	upst**air**s

Finding words

Look at the pictures below. There are five things with the same sound as **ere** in th**ere**.

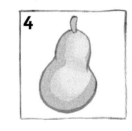

Write the five words with the same sound.

All the words can be found in the word list above.

Say the words aloud to check you have found the words with the same sound.

Using words

A Copy the passage and fill the gaps with *air*, *are*, *ear* or *ere*.

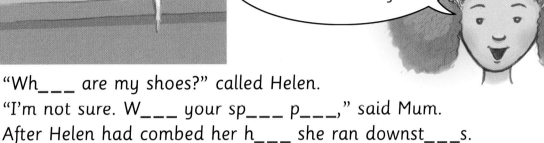

If you are not sure which letters to use, look up the words in a dictionary.

"Wh___ are my shoes?" called Helen.
"I'm not sure. W___ your sp___ p___," said Mum.
After Helen had combed her h___ she ran downst___s.
She stopped halfway down and st___d. Th___ in front of her, on the bottom st___, was her p___ of shoes.
"I'm sure they weren't th___!" she laughed.

B Add one more sentence to the passage. How many *air*, *are*, *ear* or *ere* words can you write in your sentence?

Puzzle corner

The words in a dictionary are set out **alphabetically**.

Where would you find these words in a dictionary? Copy the table and add the words below to the correct column.

If you write out the alphabet it might help you.

turtle   **yak**
monkey   **beaver**

Near the beginning	Around the middle	Towards the end

gazelle   **jackal**   **lion**
snake   **caterpillar**

Unit 9

or
ore
aw
au

caught
snore
torch
draw

born	core	crawl	autumn
fork	more	lawn	because
torch	snore	draw	caught
stork	shore	straw	naughty

Finding words

Look at the picture.
There are five things in the picture with the same sound as **or** in b**or**n.
Write the five words with the same sound.

All the words can be found in the word list.

Say the words aloud to check you have found the words with the same sound.

Using words

A Copy the sentences and fill the gaps
with **or**, **ore**, **aw** or **au**.

If you are not sure which letters to use, look up the words in a dictionary.

1 Dad's sn___ was so loud Veejay thought there was a st__m!

2 Debbie w___ her new sh__l.

3 Mark woke up at d__n bec__se he heard a h__n.

4 Jay was n__ghty – he threw s__ce on the wall.

5 Ruth y__ned as she ate her tea with a f__k.

B Write two of your own sentences.
How many **or**, **ore**, **aw** or **au** words
can you include in each sentence?

Puzzle corner

Look at these root words.

How many new words can you make by adding
the prefixes **dis** or **un** or the suffixes **ly** and **ful**.

trust

honest

like

appear

Here is one to help... unlike.

Unit 10

er ir ur

butter

purple

shirt

after	dirt	burn	computer
butter	first	purple	flower
paper	shirt	nurse	monster
sister	third	church	winter

Finding words

Look at the picture.

There are five things in the picture with the same sound as **ir** in f**ir**st.

Write the five words with the same sound.

All the words can be found in the word list.

Say the words aloud to check you have found the words with the same sound.

Using words

A Copy the sentences and fill the gaps with **er**, **ir** or **ur**.

If you are not sure which letters to use, look up the words in a dictionary.

1 Litt__ had caught against the k__b near the ch__ch.

2 Nazar was th__sty – he drank so much he thought he might b__st!

3 Lianne's little broth__ dreamt about a f__ry monst__.

4 The c__cus ret__ned to the village green.

5 A g__l fell off h__ bike and h__t h__self.

B Write two of your own sentences.
How many **er**, **ir** or **ur** words can you include in each sentence?

Puzzle corner

Look at the **dialogue words** below.
Put the best dialogue word in each gap.

| screamed | whispered | asked | moaned | said |

1 "What's the time?" _____ Hugh.

2 "Watch out!" _____ Amil.

3 "Time for tea," _____ Mum.

4 "Shh, don't wake Sarah," _____ Tim.

5 "It's raining again!" _____ Meena.

A **dialogue word** describes how someone says something.

Unit 11

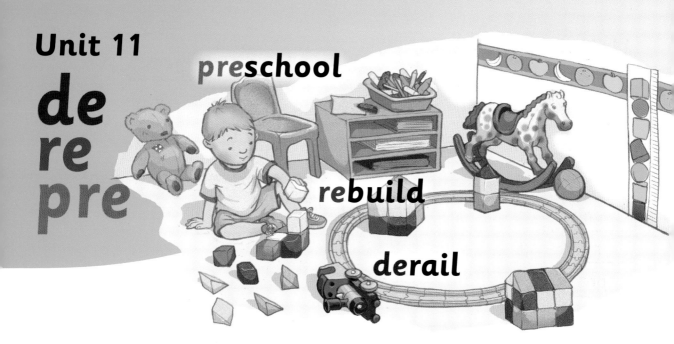

de
re
pre

preschool

rebuild

derail

decode	**re**appear	**pre**arrange	**de**tour
defrost	**re**build	**pre**packed	**re**visit
demist	**re**paint	**pre**school	**re**seal
derail	**re**start	**pre**view	**pre**historic

Finding words

A Add **de**, **re** or **pre** to each of the words to match the picture.

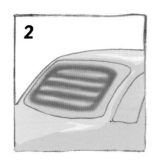

1	2	3	4
___packed	___mist	___paint	___build

The word list will help you with all of the words!

B Write each of the words you have made in a sentence.

Using words

visit

The letters **de**, **re** and **pre** are prefixes.
A **prefix** is added to the front of a word
to change its meaning.

Prefix	Meaning
de	to undo
re	to do something again
pre	to do something before

revisit

A Look at the table above.
Write a definition for each of the words.

   1 defrost   **2** reappear

   3 prearrange   **4** reseal

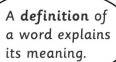

A **definition** of
a word explains
its meaning.

B Check the word definitions you
have written in a dictionary.
Copy the dictionary definition if it is
different from yours.

Puzzle corner

Write the **opposite** of each of these words.

   1 inside   dfroutsideghuy
   2 before   jsatngafterg
   3 lower   jkupperhydres
   4 polite   rudefrstwovui
   5 always   huthgeneverh
   6 difficult   heajreageasyk

I've helped by
hiding the words
in the letters!!

Unit 12

+y

stormy

rainy

dirty	cloudy	giggly	foggy
dusty	rainy	juicy	muddy
lucky	stormy	lazy	spotty
messy	windy	tasty	sunny

Finding words

A Write the word from the word list that describes each picture.

B Choose three more words from the word list.
Draw and label each word in a picture.

Using words

You need to watch out when you add **y** to some words!

wind + **y** = windy

But… when you add **y** to a word with one vowel letter before the last letter, you **double** the last letter of the word and then add **y**.

sun + **y** = sunny

one vowel letter → ← double the last letter

If a word ends in **e**, you usually drop the **e** before you add the **y**.

giggle + **y** = giggly

A Add **y** to each of these words.

   1 jump   **2** fun   **3** stripe   **4** mess

   5 trick   **6** nut   **7** fur   **8** cuddle

B Choose three of the words you have made and write each one in a sentence.

Puzzle corner

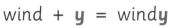

Do you remember what a **compound word** is? It's a big word that is made from two smaller words.

Write the two words each **compound word** is made from.

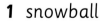

   1 snowball   **2** earache   **3** horsebox

   4 sunshine   **5** windmill   **6** somewhere

Unit 13

+ er
+ est

taller

shortest

colder	coldest	fitter	fittest
shorter	shortest	funnier	funniest
sweeter	sweetest	hotter	hottest
taller	tallest	messier	messiest

Finding words

Write the word from the word list that describes each picture.

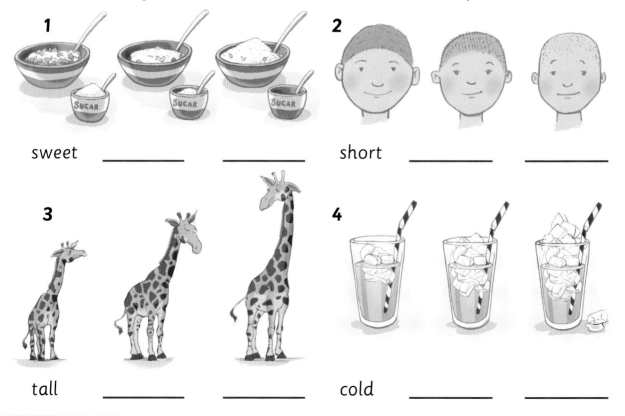

1

sweet _____ _____

2

short _____ _____

3

tall _____ _____

4

cold _____ _____

Using words

When you add **er** or **est** to words you need to think about the following things.

If a word ends in **e** just add **r** (not **er**) or **st** (not **est**).

rud<u>e</u>   rud<u>e</u>r   rud<u>e</u>st

If a word ends in **y**, change the **y** to an **i** before adding **er** or **est**.

 funn<u>y</u>   funn<u>i</u>er    funn<u>i</u>est

But... if a word has one vowel letter before the last letter, you **double** the last letter of the word and then add **er** or **est**.

 h<u>o</u>t    hot<u>t</u>er    hot<u>t</u>est

A Add **er** and **est** to each of these words.

1 sleepy   **2** big   **3** wide   **4** fast

B Choose one group of words you have just made and write them in a sentence.

Puzzle corner

Singular means one, **plural** means more than one.

fish   **boxes**

books   boat

dog   clowns

tree

Copy the words shown here.

Circle the plural words.
Write the singular words in their plural form.

One word is written the same way in its singular and plural form. Which word is it?

Unit 14

n't

won't

did**n't**	must**n't**	could**n't**	ca**n't**
is**n't**	has**n't**	should**n't**	do**n't**
was**n't**	have**n't**	would**n't**	wo**n't**

Finding words

Sometimes two words are put together to make one word.
When the words are put together a letter is squeezed out!

has + not = has**n't**

apostrophe

An **apostrophe** shows where the missing letter was.

Finish these word sums.

1 did + not = _____

2 was + not = _____

3 must + not = _____

4 do + not = _____

5 has + not = _____

6 could + not = _____

Using words

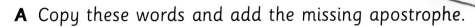

Remember the ' goes where the letter has been missed out.

A Copy these words and add the missing apostrophe.

  1 isnt   **2** wouldnt   **3** dont

  4 havent   **5** wasnt   **6** shouldnt

B Now write each word you have made in a sentence.

Did you know words using apostrophes to show missing letters are called **contractions**?

I can't get my ball!

Puzzle corner

A Match the correct definition to each word.

knowledge   a feeling of quiet and calm
peace   what people know about things
whirlwind   a large African animal with a very long neck
giraffe   a wind that spins round and round

B Write your own definition for each of these words.

  1 scissors   **2** leaflet   **3** stopwatch

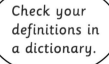

Check your definitions in a dictionary.

Is your definition as clear as the one in the dictionary?

Unit 15

silent k and w

wriggle

knee

knee	**w**rap	**k**nife	**w**hole
kneel	**w**ren	**k**night	**w**reckage
knot	**w**rist	**k**nock	**w**riggle
know	**w**rite	**k**nuckle	**w**ring

Finding words

A Add **k** or **w** to finish the word in the picture.

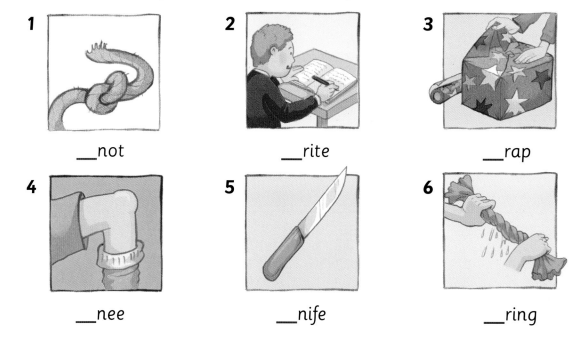

1 __not

2 __rite

3 __rap

4 __nee

5 __nife

6 __ring

B Choose three more words from the word list.
Draw and label each word in a picture.

Using words

The words in the word list each have a silent letter.

A Write these words and circle the silent letters.

> Watch out! Not all the silent letters are at the beginning of the words!

1 wrong	**2** sword	**3** knives	**4** two
5 answer	**6** knit	**7** wrote	**8** knickers

> What do you notice about the letter that follows each silent **k**?

B Write each of these words with a silent letter in a sentence.

knock   **wrapper**   **knowledge**

Puzzle corner

Add **ing** to each word.
Look at the word.
If the second to last letter is a single vowel, then the last letter usually needs to be **doubled** before adding **ing**.

shop + ing = shop**ping**

> What are we doing? The words in the box will help you.

win   **hop**   **run**
swim   **talk**   **clap**

Unit 16

+ly

lovely

lonely   **friend**ly   **cool**ly   **complete**ly
lovely   **like**ly   **real**ly   **immediate**ly
quickly   **neat**ly   **silent**ly   **separate**ly
quietly   **stupid**ly   **year**ly   **sincere**ly

Finding words

A Write the word from the word list that describes each picture.

1 n_____

2 q_____

3 f_____

4 l_____

5 q_____

6 l_____

B Write two sentences, each with a **ly** word.

Using words

ly is a suffix.
A **suffix** is a group of letters that are added to the end of a word.
A suffix helps the word 'fit' in the sentence.

Sam was <u>near</u> hit by the car.

Sam was <u>near**ly**</u> hit by the car.

Copy and change these sentences.
Add the **ly** suffix to the word in bold to make it 'fit'.

1 Ganesh's dog had a **year** check at the vets.

2 Kate was **total** confused by the sum.

3 Hugh ran **quick** to the ice-cream van.

4 Meena **kind** gave Tuhil some sweets.

5 It was **like** Kylie would get a puppy for her birthday.

Puzzle corner

Put these words in **alphabetical** order.
All the words have the same first
letter so you need to put them
in alphabetical order using the
second letter in each word.

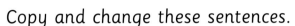

1 light
lamp
lemon

2 river
room
rabbit

3 bucket
bicycle
boot

Alphabetical order is
the order letters are
found in the alphabet.

4 firework
frog   ferry

Tip: Write out the alphabet...
it will make the Puzzle corner
activity much easier.

35

Unit 17

+ful
+less

breathless

helpful

care*ful*	end*less*	play*ful*	breath*less*
help*ful*	harm*less*	hope*ful*	taste*less*
joy*ful*	help*less*	peace*ful*	point*less*
use*ful*	pain*less*	wonder*ful*	thought*less*

Finding words

A Add **ful** or **less** to each word to match each picture.

1 use_____

2 peace_____

3 thought_____

4 hope_____

5 help_____

6 taste_____

B Write two sentences, one with a **ful** word and one with a **less** word.

Using words

ful and **less** are suffixes.
A **suffix** is a group of letters that are added to the end of a word.

A Add ful and/or **less** to each of these words.
How many different words can you make?

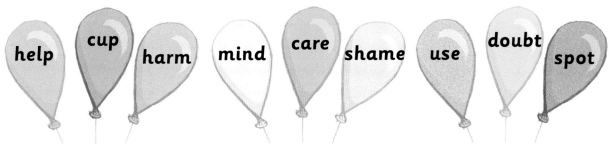

B Copy the sentence.
Use two of the words you have made to fill the gaps.

I was _____ not to spill my drink on Gran's _____ white tablecloth.

Puzzle corner

Write what you think each of the words in bold means?

1 Even though I followed the cake recipe, my result was **woeful**.

2 Regardless of keeping everyone waiting, Joe ate his pudding slowly.

3 Tom knew the grass snake was **harmless**.

Check the words in a dictionary. Were you right?

Unit 18
plurals

flies

foxes

pizzas

ants	circles	bushes	babies
drums	rectangles	churches	flies
sweets	squares	classes	knives
pizzas	triangles	foxes	wives

Finding words

When we write a word in its plural form we often just add an **s**.

A List all the things in the picture that show more than one.

Can you find the sweets?
Watch out, not all the words are in the word list!

B Add three more plural words to your list.

Using words

To make some words plural we need to do more than add **s**.

When you make words plural there are some rules to remember...

- If a word ends in **s**, **x**, **ch** or **sh** you add **es**.

atlas   atlas**es**

- If a word ends in **f** or **fe** you usually change the **f** or **fe** to a **v**, then add **es**.

thief    thie**ves**

- If a word ends in **y** with a consonant before it you change the **y** to an **i**, then add **es**.

baby   bab**ies**

Don't forget the rules above!!

Write each of these words in their plural form.

1 fly   **2** calf   **3** elephant   **4** lady   **5** class
6 fox   **7** dish   **8** rat   **9** witch   **10** knife

Puzzle corner

A **homonym** is a word with the same spelling but which has different meanings.

Copy these sentences and underline the homonyms.

1 The fly stretches its wings and has a fly every morning!

2 A tear came to the girl's eye when she found the tear on her new dress.

3 Brian found a match while watching the match.

Unit 19
mis

mis**use**

mis**hit**	mis**hear**	mis**lead**	mis**adventure**
mis**place**	mis**fire**	mis**match**	mis**behave**
mis**read**	mis**lay**	mis**time**	mis**fortune**
mis**spell**	mis**treat**	mis**use**	mis**understand**

Finding words

A Add **mis** to each of the words to match the picture.

1

JUMBLE
SAIL

_____spell

2

_____hear

3

_____hit

4

_____behave

B Choose two words from the word list, draw a picture and label each one.

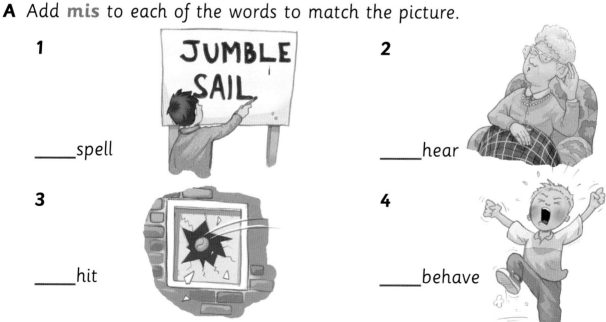

Using words

mis is a prefix.
A **prefix** is added to the front of a word to change its meaning.
The prefix **mis** means 'wrongly'.

understand   **mis**understand

A Write a sentence using each of these words.

1 behave   **2** spell
3 hear   **4** adventure

B Now add the prefix **mis** to each of the words.
Write a new sentence for each word.

Puzzle corner

Write down all the short words you can find
in each of these longer words.

Like this… misfit = **is**, **fit**, **it**

1 misfortune   **2** misunderstand
3 mishandle   **4** misspend

Have you found
all the words?
1 has six words,
2 has nine words
and **3** and **4** have
five words!

Unit 20

qu

mosquito

banquet

queen

queen	squabble	banquet	quantity
quick	square	liquid	quarrel
quilt	squeeze	mosque	quarter
quiz	squirrel	mosquito	question

Finding words

Look at the picture. There are six things in the picture with a **qu** in the spelling of the word.

Write the six **qu** words in your book.

All of the words can be found in the word list.

Using words

A Match the **qu** word to the clue.

> quantity   squeak   quit
> squeal   liquid   squaw

1 this flows out of a jug

2 a noise made by a mouse

3 the amount of something

4 to give up

5 a native North American woman

6 a long, high sound

B Choose three of the words and write each one in a sentence.

Puzzle corner

Match the **expressions** with the correct pictures.

> **Never mind!**   **Hello!**   **Thanks!**
> **Watch out!**   **Excuse me!**   **See you later!**

Unit 21

apostrophe

don't	he'll	I've	it's
didn't	I'll	they've	they're
haven't	she'll	we've	we're
shouldn't	they'll	you've	you're

Finding words

Sometimes two words are put together to make one word.
When the words are put together some letters are squeezed out!

$$she + will = she'll$$

apostrophe

An **apostrophe** shows where the missing letters were.

Match the two words with its **contraction**.
Write them together in your book.

have not	he'll
he will	they'll
they have	you're
I will	didn't
did not	they've
they are	haven't
you are	I'll
they will	they're

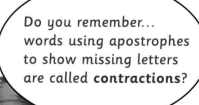

Do you remember...
words using apostrophes
to show missing letters
are called **contractions**?

Using words

A Finish these word sums.

1 you + are =
2 he + will =
3 it + is =
4 I + have =
5 they + are =
6 we + have =

B Now write each word you have made in a sentence.

Look, they're coming!

Puzzle corner

A **synonym** is a word that has the same or similar meaning to another word.
The slightly different ways we say things can be synonyms.

Look at the faces below.
Match each face with one of the synonyms in the box.

> screamed　　　laughed　　　shouted
> 　　　cried　　　whispered

1　　　2　　　3　　　4　　　5

Unit 22

non **ex** **anti**

nonstarter

antifreeze

exhaust

nonsense	**ex**change	**anti**climax	**non**believer
nonstarter	**ex**haust	**anti**clockwise	**non**drinker
nonstick	**ex**port	**anti**freeze	**non**member
nonstop	**ex**press	**anti**septic	**non**payment

Finding words

Add **non**, **ex** or **anti** to each of these words.

1

____stick

2

____change

3
____member

4
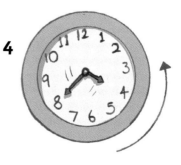
____clockwise

Using words

The letters **non**, **ex** and **anti** are prefixes.
A **prefix** is added to the front of a word to change its meaning.

   ex + port = **ex**port (take 'out of port')

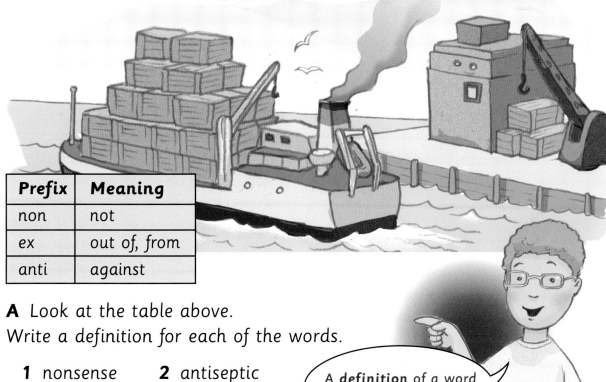

Prefix	Meaning
non	not
ex	out of, from
anti	against

A Look at the table above.
Write a definition for each of the words.

   1 nonsense   **2** antiseptic
   3 exchange   **4** export

A **definition** of a word explains its meaning.

B Check the word definitions you have written in a dictionary.
Copy the dictionary definition if it is different from yours.

Puzzle corner

Choose three more words from the word list.
Look up each word in a dictionary.
Does it have more than one meaning?

Now draw and label three pictures of the words.
Each picture needs to clearly show what each
word means.

Spelling Challenge

Write a word that uses each of these sounds or letter patterns.

You have practised all the sounds and letter patterns in this book!

1 er, ir, ur	**2** ee, ea
3 + y	**4** mis
5 qu	**6** a–e, ai, ay
7 de, re, pre	**8** o–e, oa, ow
9 le	**10** un, dis
11 or, ore, aw, au	**12** n't
13 silent k, silent w	**14** + ly
15 ie, i–e, y, igh	**16** + er, + est
17 + ful, + less	**18** non, ex, anti
19 oo, ew, u–e, ue	**20** air, are, ear, ere

Well done, you have now finished this book. We hope it has helped you with your spellings.